Hope you enjoy

Isobel

Growing Up Rural

Isobel Eastman

Rural Press

Published by Rural Press
5982 Prince of Wales Drive
North Gower, ON
K0A 2T0
Tel: 613-489-3276

Library and Archives Canada Cataloguing in Publication

Eastman, Isobel, 1935-
Growing up rural/Isobel Eastman

ISBN 978-0-9687544-1-2

1. Eastman, Isobel, 1935--Childhood and youth.
2. Farm life--Ontario--Lanark (County)--History.
3. Lanark (Ont. : County)--Biography. I. Kenney, Elaine, 1949-
II. Title.

FC3095.L37Z49 2007 630'.92
C2007-901979-X

Publication consulting and editing by
Elaine Kenney, Communication Matters, Ottawa

Cover and book design by
Terry Corrigan, TKC Creative Communications, Ottawa

Printed and bound in Canada byTranscontinental

Growing Up Rural is dedicated to Murray Hartin

I dedicate this book to Murray Hartin, as it was Murray who inspired me to start writing again. After having completed three books, *When We Were Just Born, Out of the Mouths of Babes* and *Rural Reflections,* I had become lazy and had taken a sabbatical from writing. Then, one day, Murray and I started to reminisce about our school days. Based on the stories he told me about his growing up years, I discovered that he had been a real little imp and must have tested the mettle of his teachers. As he was telling me about his schoolboy pranks, I felt inspired and sensed the beginnings of another book! These stories, that I felt needed to be told, are the stories in *Growing Up Rural.* Many of them feature Matt and his cronies, but they are based on Murray and his buddies. And of course, some literary licence is added to these tales.

My only regret is that Murray did not live to see these stories in print, but I am sure that his family will enjoy them. I am proud to dedicate this book to Murray Hartin, a fun person and a good friend.

About Murray Hartin

Murray Hartin was born on October 19, 1937. He died at the age of 64 on July 21, 2002. He had a full life, but it was much too short.

His parents, Ercil and Erma Hartin, raised their seven children on a farm on Richmond Road. Murray was the third youngest of that large family. They all attended School Section # 7 in Nepean. Murray attended Ottawa Technical High School for Grade nine, but when the construction of South Carleton High School was completed, he returned there to graduate from Grade 12. He attended Hydro School in Toronto and trained to become an electrician and a lineman. It was his job to climb those high towers and do repair work.

When attending South Carleton High School he met the love of his life, Helen Scott. They married on September 29, 1962 and settled in Manotick where Murray became involved in the church and community. He also became a doting parent of two children, Heather and Bonnie. Many years later, more joy was added to his life with the addition of three grandchildren, Emma and Andrew Avon and Olivia Fiarchuk. (A third grandchild, Trinity Fiarchuk, was born after Murray's death.)

Murray was diagnosed with Multiple Sclerosis in 1988 so his activities had to be curtailed. But like the endearing character in this book, Matt, Murray always had a sparkle in his eye and maintained his mischievous trademark traits that defined who he was for as long as he lived.

Boyhood Memories

We traveled together in our pre-highschool years
Filled with happiness and rarely some tears
Full of innocence and willing to learn
We sure loved to eat, we had energy to burn.

Murray was really an actor, who didn't need a stage
He brought joy to all, regardless of their age
If you craved for applause, you joined him in a skit
Ad-libbing his lines, gave the teacher a fit.

With the strength of a high spirited steed, yet the gentleness of a lamb
Murray would offer his assistance, plus the leadership of a ram
One day while adventuring at the mature age of nine,
I was seriously injured: It was the end of the line
My hero saved me. Murray carried me for a mile.
His reward for his efforts, why, cookies and a smile.

While attending grade ten, Murray's behaviour changed gears
Suddenly he matured, far beyond his boyish years
A little lady from Manotick stole his big heart away
Which she still holds dearly, each and every day
Although he's gone forever, Murray's legacy will remain
Sharing our youthful years was certainly my gain.

Only his closest young friends, always called him "MUZZ"
I don't know why, maybe or just because...

John Davidson

"His generous spirit, sense of humour and creativity has touched the lives of relatives and many friends." In Memoriam

TABLE OF CONTENTS

When I was growing up on a dairy farm in Lanark County during the 1940s and 1950s it was easier to define rural. If you didn't live in town you were considered rural and lived on a working farm. Back then there was often a sense of romance connected to country living. Being a farmer meant you were your own boss and had a certain amount of freedom. But for those farmers who worked long hours for little money the romantic side was less apparent. Rural people lacked many of the comforts that people in town had such as hydro, indoor plumbing and the luxury of having the weekends off.

On our dairy farm, my father was also involved in fur farming. We raised foxes, mink and chinchillas. Eventually the bottom fell out of the fox and chinchilla market as women no longer wanted long-haired fur coats. My dad said it was a risky business to be in a livelihood that depended on the whims of women!

We lived on the old homestead that my grandfather lived on as a young boy. His family had emigrated from Ireland during the potato famine. My siblings and I grew up in the same small log house covered over with clapboards and filled with love.

Because it was a rather large farming operation, we had several men working and living at our place. We were never allowed to call them the "hired men" as my parents thought that was a derogatory term. They were treated like part of the family and always kept in touch after they left. I can recall one winter when we had five men working on the farm. I remember too, when at night they would pitch in and help Mom peel the potatoes and prepare the vegetables that were then left overnight in a cream can filled with water, ready to be cooked for the following day's big noon meal. All Mom had to do the next morning was to make four or five pies, keep up with the laundry, do the cleaning and raise four kids. Is it any wonder that Mom always seemed to be tired? In the evening, after the chores were done, we all gathered around the big table and played games such as crokinole, Chinese checkers and card games. Games were very much a part of family life back then.

During the war years, it was often difficult to get farm labourers. At one point we had two German prisoners of war working for us. They were very young, very blonde, spoke no English and appeared quite lonely. They wore dark shirts with a big bull's eye on the back. Even as a child I dreaded what that meant. I recall my mother saying to us that somewhere in Germany there were two mothers wondering where their boys were and if they were safe.

After the war we had a Dutch boy come over to work with us on a farm program. His name was Appie and in his limited English he told my dad that he was a "cartner". My dad interpreted that to mean he was a carpenter and said, *"Oh, we can really use a carpenter around here to help repair things."* Dad was ready to send him out with some tools to repair a fence. Appie replied, *"No, no not a carpenter—a cartner."* Because Appie couldn't understand English, my dad believed that if he spoke louder, Appie would understand better. Their conversation soon deteriorated and the verbal exchange became a louder and louder shouting match, with Appie quietly shrugging his shoulders. We eventually determined that he was a gardener!

Not long ago my sister and I discovered that Appie owned a flower shop in Pickering, so we decided to pay him a visit. A young man, the very image of Appie, was unloading flowers from a van. I asked him if he was Appie's son. He replied that he was and took us into the store to meet his dad, where we had a great visit with him. Appie found it to be an interesting coincidence that the very day we visited him, it was his 40th anniversary of having arrived at our farm from Holland. He recalled how patient my dad was with him, his limited farming experience at that time and the shouting matches! He reminded me that he had often helped me with my math homework.

As a child, I was a bit of a dreamer and created many pictures in my mind gleaned from the books that I had read and the movies I had seen. One image I had was of beautiful girls running barefoot through the fields of hay with their long hair tossing in the wind. I wanted to be one of those girls. After all, here I was in the country, and I had plenty of fields to run through. One day, I had just arrived home—it was the last day of school and my birthday. In hindsight, my mom must have wanted to get rid of me for a little while. She told me to run out to the field and show my dad my report card. Here was my opportunity! I went barefoot down the lane, which was fine because it was fairly smooth and my feet were really tough. But when I got to the hay field, it was another story—the field was full of stubble from the newly mowed hay. This is where the beautiful picture I had in my mind went awry. The stubble was really sharp, my dad was at the other end of the field, my feet hurt from the prickly hay and my hair refused to blow in the wind because it was short and curly. This reality was nothing like my fantasy. I showed my report card to my dad, who was dutifully impressed and then limped all the way back to the house.

All the children at that time went to school in a one-room school house. They were the best of times and the worst of times. In those days, the teacher didn't stay at school for the lunch hour but walked the quarter of a mile back to her boarding place, leaving her 20 or so students unsupervised. During this time we always organized some game or other. One day we made a teeter totter in the woodshed using an old stump and a plank of wood. This is how it worked. While one person stood on the low end of the plank, another would climb up onto a beam in the woodshed above the teeter totter, jump onto the high end of the plank, sending the person on the low end flying up into the air to grab onto the beam. It was a great lesson on levers and physics and usually worked quite well. However, one day the person who was supposed to fly through the air missed the beam and broke his arm. That ended that particular activity!

During the war years, we often spent the afternoons at school gathering milkweed pods from the neighbouring farmers' fields. It was a part of the highly promoted war effort. The milkweed silk was supposed to be used to manufacture parachute material. We gathered bag after bag after bag of the pods and felt so patriotic. It wasn't until about two years ago that I heard an interview on the radio about the milkweed pods. Someone stated that the project was unsuccessful—the milkweed pods were unuseable to make parachutes. There were, however, winners in this war effort—the farmers who got rid of the weeds and, of course, us students who didn't mind getting out of school work to pick the milkweed.

Today's educators probably shudder when they

contemplate the idea of the one-room schoolhouse with its limited facilities and supplies. Everyone who has attended one, I am sure, has a funny story to tell about either the frozen water, the pot bellied stoves, the wet, smelly, woolen mitts hung around the stove, the ink well tricks or the antics at recess.

There are many good things that I recall from my experiences in a one-room schoolhouse. It was there that I was introduced to a love of reading. At the end of each day the teacher read a chapter from a novel. No matter how old the students were, we all listened with rapt attention. Within this environment there was also a real sense of community, where the older students looked after the little ones. This is the more idyllic picture of the one-room schoolhouse, but there was another side that I also recall related to the universal mischievousness of children.

I remember hiding behind trees where we wrapped dried cedar needles in paper and smoked them like cigarettes. I remember wandering all over the neighbourhood, playing a game of Run Sheep Run, and ignoring the bell that called us back to the schoolhouse until the game was completed. School was also the place where I was first exposed to cuss words. A girl, a fellow student who I really idolized, swore a lot saying, *"Oh God this,"* and *"Oh God that,"* among other choice phrases. We were never allowed to talk like that at home. The strongest words I had ever heard my mom utter were, *"Holy Moses!"* And that was only on a really bad day! My sister continually told me I'd be going to hell if I used God's name in vain and other curse words. She seemed to be an expert in hell because she was very certain that I was going there. Being a very inventive child, I would say, *"Oh dog this,"* and, *"Oh dog that!"* It wasn't really cursing because dog was God spelled backwards and that wasn't wrong, but it made me feel almost as important as my cursing friend!

As well as the school, our little country church in Blakeney was a focal point of rural life. During one afternoon service a man burst into the church and yelled that the McDougal place was on fire. All the men quickly left to help fight the fire. Only the women, children and the minister were left. The minister carried on as usual but as a little kid I wondered who would take up the offering. There were no men and only men took up the offering! However, at the appropriate moment, the oldest member of our congregation, Mrs. Giles, rose with dignity and took up the collection on both sides of the church all by herself. We were such slaves to tradition. I remember thinking that perhaps the money was a little tainted because it was presented by a woman. I've come a long way since then!

The children's time with the minister was always a risky business. You just never knew what they would say. Once the minister asked the children what they thought Jesus was like. A little three-year-old boy replied, *"Oh, my mommy won't let me say that word!"* The minister assured him that it was fine to say that word in church.

One Sunday we had friends of the family visiting. They were partners with my dad in the fur business and they had just been paid for a shipment of fox furs. One couple had a five-year-old son, Sandy. They all accompanied us to church that day. When the collection plate was passed, we were amazed when Sandy deposited a hundred dollar bill on the plate. His father was even more surprised. Apparently, Sandy had been into his father's wallet and helped himself to some of Dad's hard-earned fur money.

After high school, I left my community to become a kindergarten teacher. My first school was at Goodstown just outside of Richmond. It was quite an experience and I'm still shocked at how innocent and naive I was—one could almost say dumb! During the first week of school I broke three yardsticks by pounding them on the floor to maintain order. And that same year I never used the outside toilet until after the school day was over and I was sure all the children had gone home. I had heard too many tales about kids upsetting the outhouse with the teacher inside it!

Every year at Christmas time I had the children dramatize the Christmas Story for their parents. One year, I chose Terry to play the role of Joseph. He was a big boy with a deep voice. He was supposed to look at Mary holding the baby Jesus in her arms and say to her, *"That's a nice baby we have Mary. He looks just like his mother."* That's the way we had practiced it, but that's not what came out. Terry put his hands on his hips and in his big, deep voice said, *"That's a nice baby you got there Mary. He looks just like your mother!"*

After teaching for 30 years, I decided it was time to retire when I heard that the grandchild of a student I had taught during my first year would be in my next year's kindergarten class.

Another great treasure of rural life was the party line. I am sure that some people can still recall their particular ring—it could have been five long ones and two short ones. An aunt and uncle of mine lived just across the road from us. My auntie had a bad habit of listening on the party line, particularly when it rang for her neighbour, Ethel, who lived down the road. When she heard two long rings and one short one, that meant that someone was calling Ethel. Auntie figured that she might hear some worthwhile news. It was a relatively harmless habit and it certainly filled the days for Auntie who didn't drive and who was at home all the time. However, Auntie probably never realized that she was not being very subtle about it. Her phone was directly under her big wall clock and in those days clocks actually went tick-tock. People always knew when Auntie was listening—they could hear her wall clock going tick-tock in the background.

Back then, one long continuous ring on the phone meant an emergency—a death or a fire—and then of course everyone picked up the phone. That is how we were informed about the terrible Almonte train wreck.

In those days it was tricky getting a phone call from your boyfriend because you had to be cautious about who was listening. You could usually tell if there was a third party on the line because the sound was a bit diluted. I remember dearly wanting to grow up and be a Bell telephone operator and learn how to plug in all those doodads that connected people together. Just another of my many unfulfilled fantasies!

I grew up on a farm, taught in rural schools, married and raised a family in the country and attended a small rural church. All these experiences have contributed to the life I continue to love. My life, my choice—I am truly blessed with Growing Up Rural.

Rascals

Matt yelled for his mom. *"Mawm, Mawm! Me and Jake are goin' to the swimmin' hole. Okay?"* Matt didn't call his mother Mom or Mum, but used his own Ottawa Valley twang that came out as, *"Mawm"*.

His mother returned the call. *"Be back for lunch and watch out for the snapper!"*

Matt's mom always warned him about the snapping turtle that was legend in the creek. Matt referred to the creek as the swimmin' hole. No one in recent times had spotted the turtle but that just added to the mystery surrounding the reptile. It was rumoured to be very old and cranky. Swimmers were warned that it might snap at their toes if disturbed. How the young boys wished that the snapper would appear so they could have the most recent bragging rights! Matt acknowledged his mother's warning and he and Jake headed off for the creek. He carried his towel and a box of straws taken from the kitchen cupboard. He didn't mention the straws to his mom. No need to call her attention to them—she might not approve of their plans.

Matt was a rascal! He was the kind of kid that

usually got into trouble, not major trouble, but mischievous trouble. His unruly reddish hair always seemed to be in need of a trim and his freckles became more prominent when he blushed. And he blushed often. He blushed when he was accused of a misdeed and he blushed whether he was guilty *or* innocent. He was completely incapable of lying and was a typical Norman Rockwell type of kid, someone in fact who could look innocent and guilty at the same time.

On the way to the creek, Jake and Matt discussed what they would do if they ever saw the snapper. Jake knew that some high-class restaurants served turtle soup and if the snapper was as large as folklore had it, they might make a bundle of money by selling it to these establishments. Matt determined that if turtle soup was in such demand it would be even a better idea to keep the turtle and raise baby turtles to ensure a continuing supply for the fancy restaurants. The plan broke down, though, when they weren't quite sure how they would go about ensuring a steady supply of baby turtles.

Their thoughts went back to their task at hand—the straws, the creek and the search for bullfrogs. They flung their pants and their towels on the ground and dove into the creek. The water was cool and murky. They couldn't see their hands in front of them as they swam and it got even worse when the water was stirred up.

The pond was full of bullfrogs and that was their main focus now—to find two bullfrogs. They weren't easy to catch as they were slippery and would want to be free from the clutches of these two boys. Jake and Matt got out of the water and set up watch on the bank of the creek, whispering now, so they wouldn't frighten away the frogs.

Bullfrogs were heard before they were seen. A deep "garrumph" signaled their presence but locating their sound didn't guarantee they would be caught. Nature had provided them with such good camouflage that it made it difficult to spot them. Finally Jake saw one. Down the creek, on the branch of a tree that lay in the water was one big, old, fat bullfrog and there on a lily pad just beside the branch was another one the same size.

Matt and Jake were experts in the art of catching frogs—they had a distinct strategy. First, they positioned themselves so they were just behind the frogs. With a swift motion they each captured a bullfrog by grabbing them and holding on tightly to their long slippery legs; they then transferred their grip to hold the frogs more securely. They didn't want to hurt the frogs—that was not their intention at all.

The next step in the process required two people per frog. Matt reached for his pants that were lying on the ground and put his bullfrog in one of the pockets, securing it, so there was no chance of it escaping. He then went to help Jake with his frog, holding it, but not too tightly—you had to know just how much pressure to exert—while Jake inserted a straw into its hind end and blew into the straw. When the belly of the frog was puffed up like a balloon, he withdrew the straw and quickly released the frog onto the creek. It skimmed over the water, in a jet propelled fashion, as the air was expelled from its body. The rascals repeated the procedure with Matt's frog. They then noted how far each frog had gone before it started to swim normally. The winner of the contest was determined by the frog which went the farthest. The sound of their laughter filled the air as they watched the frogs zoom across the water. They played the game several more times until they ran out of bullfrogs.

The boys knew it was getting near lunch time because the sun was almost directly overhead, so they took a few minutes to have a quick swim. Suddenly, Matt screamed as his foot touched something sharp in the murky water. *"The snapper's got me! Help!"*

The boys leaped out of the water and, like a flash, disappeared down the road to Matt's home. They left their pants, their towels and the box of straws by the creek and were happy to distance themselves from what they thought was the legendary snapper. Gone was their bravado! Gone were their plans for becoming rich from turtle soup. Their main objective was to put distance between them and the snapper.

When they reached home they both started talking at once, telling Matt's mom that they had been attacked by the snapper. Mom inspected Matt's foot and found no injury. She went on to inspect his leg where she detected only a small scratch on the calf. It looked to her as if a branch had "bitten" him; she applied a band-aid and proceeded to pull off a few leeches that were still clinging to his legs. The creek was full of leeches and they were used to them, but they couldn't stop talking about the close call they had with the snapper. They had a big story to tell the other kids at school on Monday.

As they relived their experience at the creek, they made plans to catch the turtle and decided that a lasso was probably the surest method. In preparation for the hunt, they got a rope from the garage and started practicing their roping skills.

Just at that moment, Mom called them in for lunch. She told the boys to help themselves while she retrieved the straws from the cupboard for their chocolate milk.

Matt and Jake looked at each other, remembering that the box of straws was still down by the creek. *"Don't trouble yourself Mawm, we don't need straws today."*

Jenn's Bike

Jenn awoke with anticipation on the morning of her eighth birthday. Maybe, just maybe, her hopes wouldn't be dampened by Mom's perennial warning that preceded every birthday and Christmas. *"There isn't much money so gifts will be sparse. After all, times are tough!"* This blanket statement applied not only to birthdays and Christmas but to just about any occasion where gifts were a possibility.

Jenn, the eternal optimist, was up quickly and bounced down the stairs. Once in the kitchen, she feigned nonchalance, but her growing excitement failed to stop her little heart from going pit-a-pat. Breakfast held absolutely no appeal for her that morning. It was a family rule, though, that everyone ate together and no gifts were given until *after* breakfast. Jenn paced the kitchen, looking towards the barn. What was keeping her dad?

To no one in particular she exclaimed, *"This is probably the time that Betsy, that stupid heifer, will choose to have her baby! And wouldn't you know it, on my birthday!"* Her comments failed to attract sympathy.

They did, however, attract an undesired response from her older brother, Matt, who started up his teasing.

"Lucky you. We could call the calf, Jenn, in your honour. Wouldn't that be fun? When people talked about Jenn, I wouldn't know who they were referring to—the cow or you. You'd both look alike too!"

Jenn picked up a large, heavy cushion and pegged it at Matt, hitting him squarely in the belly, winding him for a minute so he had to give up the teasing. Matt was continually trying to get a rise out of Jenn but at eight years old she was learning the smarts that saved her from falling into his trap.

Dad finally came in from the barn to wash up and sit down for breakfast, seemingly taking forever to accomplish these small tasks. And wouldn't you know it, Mom had cooked some pancakes especially for the occasion. Jenn loved pancakes, but they took time to finish. Jenn wanted to shove down the food as quickly as possible and get to her presents. She had high hopes for a special gift this year—something she had been wanting for a long time. The family took their time eating while small talk prevailed. It was all on purpose: they knew it and she knew it.

"What's on for today, kids?" asked Dad innocently.

"Oh nothing much," said Matt, *"just school and then Rick and I are going fishing."*

Dad turned to Jenn. *"What about you Jenn? Anything special on today?"*

Jenn had taken all she could and asserted, *"It's my birthday you guys for goodness sakes! Quit fooling around and let's get down to birthday things. What about the presents?"*

Mother patted her on the head, gave her a hug and presented her with a parcel that Grandma had sent. Jenn unwrapped it with expectation and was surprised to find a serviceable pair of pink pyjamas. She held them up to check for size. She was even more surprised! Grandma must have forgotten that she had grown over the year; the pyjama bottoms reached just below her knees.

"Can we send them back and get the right size?" Jenn asked.

"I don't think so," Mom explained, *"Grandma's getting older and she'd be so disappointed. Besides, she probably didn't keep the bill anyway."* The pyjamas were put to one side and Jenn waited expectantly for the next gift. Matt pulled up a scrunched up, sloppily wrapped parcel out from under the table.

"Happy birthday squirt!" he said.

Jenn hastily unwrapped the mess of a parcel and found a bright, shiny fishing lure, just like the one that Matt had been admiring at Home Hardware. She liked to fish, but wondered whose birthday it was, hers or Matt's? She mumbled a disappointed thank-you. Matt assured her that if she didn't like the lure, he could use it and he'd be happy to find her another one. Matt then suggested that she take another look through the wrapping paper. She was delighted with what she found—a pretty bracelet that she had longed for for awhile. This time, she thanked Matt enthusiastically.

One more present to go! She waited anxiously for Mom and Dad to proffer their gift. Dad took his time and Mom reminded Jenn, *"Money is tight and don't expect too much."* They explained that the gift had just come in from Home Hardware the other night and they hadn't had time to assemble it. Dad went to the woodshed and with Matt's help dragged a big box into the kitchen. At last, Jenn thought, this must be the bicycle that she so desperately wanted and had been hinting for.

But there, on the front of the box was a picture of a baby stroller with directions on how to assemble it. Matt began to laugh hysterically while rolling on the floor.

Dad, with a puzzled look, sputtered and wondered how this could have happened. *"We ordered a bike, but this sure is no bike! Don't worry, we'll get this all straightened out. How could they have mixed up a bike with a baby stroller?"*

Jenn went to bed that night and relived her birthday and the surprises it brought: a pair of too-small pyjamas, a fishing lure and a baby stroller. Who would have thought! Matt, even though he was a tease, wasn't all bad—he had chosen just the thing for her—a lovely bracelet! And, besides, Mom's perennial warning hadn't really applied this year—Jenn would soon have a brand-new, shiny bicycle—the very thing she had hoped for. This year certainly augured for better things to come. Perhaps times weren't as "tough" as they used to be. She looked forward to next year, when she turned nine. Being an optimist certainly had its advantages.

Matt Does It Again

There were no dreaded baby strollers for Jenn this Christmas, not a one! After the big foul-up of having mistakenly received a stroller for her eighth birthday last year, she finally was able to gaze upon her brand new, long-awaited bike this Christmas morning. Dad had even taken the time to assemble it on Christmas Eve. It was painted a lovely bright green colour, and appropriately named the Green Tornado. The addition of special decals made it appear as if it was racing with the wind.

She could hardly wait to try out the Green Tornado. But this wintery Christmas was no different from most others, with snow on the ground, there was no opportunity for her to ride the bike outside. But if winter comes, can spring be far behind? And when spring comes the warm days of summer are certain to follow. For now, Jenn's vision of streaking down the road on the Green Tornado was almost enough to keep her content, but not quite.

For the time being, Jenn had to be satisfied with trying the bike out in the basement. Dad had cleared his junk to one area, leaving an open space for both Jenn and her brother, Matt, to play in. The area soon became a modified Indy 500 track. The very tight circle challenged them to maneuver their bikes around it without falling.

Matt constantly tried to push the envelope by attempting time and again to get Jenn to allow him a try on the Green Tornado. He pleaded, begged and promised, *"It would only be for a short ride."* Matt also resorted to attempts at bribing Jenn with his hockey card collection, his special magic rock that he treasured and even his half-full piggy bank. Jenn resisted. She had become immune to his pleading, begging and bribing and remained steadfast, rebuffing all his pleas. To add to Jenn's position, their parents had forbidden Matt to ride Jenn's special machine. This was a stern reproach, but necessary because Matt seemed to break everything he touched!

Slowly the days passed and spring finally came. The mud dried up and the bikes could go outside. What a feeling of freedom it offered Jenn! At last she could give the Green Tornado a real road test. The bike proved to be a wonderful machine. In no time at all Jenn was popping wheelies, riding with no hands and learning the tricks that Matt had mastered on his own bike.

Finally the day came when Jenn posed the question, *"Mom, can we ride our bikes to school today?"* She had even prepared arguments for her case because she was sure her mom would refuse her request.

"I don't see why not," replied Mom, *"the roads are good and you have been very responsible with your new bike."*

They were allowed! Matt and Jenn looked at each other with surprise and quickly hopped on their bikes before their mom could change her mind.

"Just don't let anyone else ride Tornado, Jenn. The others will all want a turn on it, but best you just ride it yourself for a while." That was her mom's only stipulation and Jenn agreed that it was a fair one.

Jenn and Matt went off to school in high spirits. The Green Tornado was living up to its name. As well as keeping up with Matt, she was able to attempt some fancy wheeling on the mile-long road to school. The road had just been freshly graded leaving loose gravel on each side, making riding a bit tricky. About half-way to school Jenn's wheels got caught in the gravel and she spun out of control, swerving from side to side and finally landing on her bottom. Tornado went crashing on its side. Quickly, Matt stopped to help his sister. Jenn didn't bother to look at her scrapes; her first concern was her bike. Jenn and Matt both inspected it, looking for damage. Everything seemed to be intact, so they continued on their journey to school and upon arrival everyone gathered around to admire the bike that Jenn had so often talked about.

"So this is your new bike?"
"Wow, is it ever a beauty!"
"Now I know why you call it the Green Tornado!"
"It really looks like it's built for speed!"
"I bet you can go faster than Matt!"
"Can I have a turn on it?"

Jenn remembered her mom's stipulation that only she could ride the bike. Fortunately, the school bell rang. She was saved from denying her friends a turn on the bike. She would deal with that problem at noon hour. When noon hour finally did arrive, Jenn and her girlfriends spent their time comparing notes on the math exam they had just endured. Luckily for Jenn, at least for the time being, the bike was not mentioned.

During this same time, the boys were busy constructing a ramp out of scrap lumber they had scavenged from the woodshed. The idea of the ramp had been inspired by Evil Kneivel, the daring motorcycle stunt driver. It was Matt's idea to duplicate Evil's stunts but on a smaller scale. With a few more nails in the ramp it would be secure enough and ready for the first trial run. The boys' objective was to approach the ramp at a high speed on their bikes and see how far they could fly through the air before landing upright on their bikes.

Glenn was chosen to do the first trial run at a slow speed to see if the ramp had the proper angle. He landed safely but didn't have much air time. Several other boys tried it with varying results. Finally, it was Matt's turn. Just as he was about to start his approach to the ramp, Glenn shouted, *"Matt, your back tire is flat."*

Matt got off his bike and looked with disgust at his back tire. It was as flat as a pancake. Matt had really wanted a turn at the ramp, after all, it was his brainchild. To add insult to injury, he thought of the long walk home after school with Jenn speeding down the road on her Green Tornado and he with his useless machine. What rotten luck!

Then he had an evil thought. Jenn was busy with her friends. He could use her new bike for his turn and she would never know the difference. Keeping an eye out for his sister, he removed the bike from the rack and slipped stealthily to the back of the school and the ramp.

He mounted the bike, pedaled furiously and made a wide swath so he could build up speed for the approach to the ramp. The Tornado responded. Over the ramp and up into the air he went with lots of hang time. He really felt like Evil Kneivel as he soared through the air. He positioned himself for the landing and felt the front tire hit the ground. The bike gave a sudden twist and he found himself with his face to the ground and the Green Tornado on top of him. That is, most of it was on top of him. Out of the corner of his eye he could see the back wheel lying separately in a twisted, unnatural position. His scratches and sore back caused him no grief compared to the deep trouble he knew he was in.

Jenn came running with her friends to see what the ruckus was all about. She couldn't believe her eyes.

"Matt!" she screamed, *"what have you done to my new bike? You big pig. You've broken it! My brand new bike! You weren't to touch it! Don't you ever do what you're told?"*

In his mind, Matt could hear his parents saying those very same words. He had done it again! But this time he had really messed up. He didn't blame Jenn for being angry.

The remainder of the school day dragged by slowly and neither Jenn nor Matt were able to concentrate on their work. On the way home, Jenn rode Matt's bike and he pushed the wounded Tornado as best he could in its state of disrepair. Jenn rode ahead of him, circling back every now and then to confront him and declare his stupidity.

Matt was punished for his brief, ill-fated ride on Jenn's new bike. His sister would use his bike until he saved up enough money to repair the damage done to the Green Tornado. He reluctantly agreed that it was a fair punishment.

While Matt walked to and from school during this punitive period, it allowed him time to reassess the whole affair. He decided that the ramp idea really was a good one and the only problem was that he hadn't faced the ramp squarely enough on take off. He could also probably get more hang time if his approach was a little longer and he used more speed on takeoff. He wouldn't make those mistakes again.

During this walking time he also thought seriously about all the different times he had found himself in trouble. It wasn't always his fault. In fact, he felt he was usually blameless and it was more bad luck than anything else. In spite of this, in one of his more reflective, responsible moments he made himself a promise that he would try to stay out of trouble for the rest of the year. On second thought, maybe for just the rest of this month. That, at least, would be much more realistic!

The Bike Race

"You stand guard today, Glenn, and make sure you watch for her comin' back! You hear now?" Those were the orders for Glenn who was the odd man out for the day. It was his job to watch for the teacher who would be coming back to school after her lunch break in about an hour and a half. It was the custom in the 1940s for the teacher to go to her boarding house at noon for lunch. This day, she left her 26 students at School Section No. 7 unsupervised, which was also the custom.

Glenn was well informed about the responsibilities of the one chosen to act as lookout. And he was well aware of the importance of his job. However, this responsibility meant that he couldn't take part in the planned devilment. And he dearly loved the illicit activities devised by the older boys. Because of his small stature, he was the one who was chosen to squeeze into areas not accessible by the others. They often called on him too, to be an accomplice, but not today. Someone was required to stand watch and it was his turn.

Today's event in the one-room schoolhouse involved moving all of the desks to the centre of the room. Everyone helped, even Glenn and the younger children. As the desks were being moved, a few papers spilled out onto the floor, but they were quickly shoved back and not always into the proper desk!

A time keeper was appointed. Today it was Janey because she had just received a brand new watch for her birthday, a watch that had a second hand on it. No longer did the children have to depend on the big wall clock that had no second hand. Now, the time scores would be much more precise.

The competitors in today's contest went outside and brought their bikes into the classroom. They checked their bike chains and rolled up their pant legs. Matt and Grant were fortunate—they had fancy pant clips that tucked their pant legs safely out of the way of the chains. Before having the pant clips, they had carelessly ruined several pants by not keeping the legs rolled up. Their parents had decided that the clips were cheaper items to purchase than constantly replacing pants.

Glenn, the lookout, had nominated Bob to do a trial run for today's event. The object of the game was for the competitors to ride their bikes, as quickly as possible, by circling around the desks without falling. It was a very tight racing oval, but offered fun and excitement for the students at School Section No. 7. Bob mounted his bike and started off on his trial run. He only got half-way around when he ran into one of the desks. His collision pointed to some required changes. Desks needed to be rearranged and the track readjusted. Bob then tried it again, maneuvering successfully around the oval this time. The task of doing a trial run was imperative to the success of the game and Bob was pleased to have been chosen.

Grant, Matt and Emma were ready to do their runs in that order. They proceeded to get their bikes ready to go: they checked the chains, tried the brakes, kicked the tires, and the boys put on their pant clips. Janey had her eyes on her new watch. Everyone waited for her to raise her arm to signal the beginning of the race.

Grant mounted his bike, a machine that had "Turbo" emblazoned on the fenders. He had modified the bike by lowering the seat, thinking that this alteration made him more aerodynamic as he crouched over the handlebars. Janey waited until the second hand was pointing precisely at 12:00 o'clock, before lowering her arm and yelling, *"Go!"*

Grant took off like a bullet and rounded the first corner successfully. He leaned his body to the inside of the track, rounded the second corner, made the third corner without a problem and headed for the finish line where Janey waited with watch in hand.

"Wow, was I ever traveling! That must have been my best run in ages." Grant looked expectantly at Janey who checked his time. He was looking forward to making record time. *"Twenty-five seconds,"* Janey announced.

Grant moaned. *"Come on Janey. I was faster than that. What's wrong with your stupid watch?"*

Everyone yelled at him not to be such a sore loser as he walked away, visibly disappointed. He joined the others in the centre of the room but continued to mutter about Janey's inaccurate watch.

Matt was now at the starting line and ready to go. He gave his bike tires one last kick—it was the macho thing to do. His bike was bright red with racing stripes painted on the fenders. Matt had done the painting himself, so the stripes were a little wiggly, but the general effect was one of speed.

The second hand approached 12:00 o'clock and Janey once again yelled, *"Go!"*

Matt made the first corner, headed into the second one and seemed to be going faster than Grant as he leaned into the third corner. Everyone was cheering and yelling, *"Go, Matt, go!"*

Just then, Sandra "accidently" shoved a book onto the floor right into his path and Matt wiped out. The bike went crashing into the desks along with Matt. He tried using his arms to protect himself, but his right elbow took the impact. When it started to bleed, the sight of it made him howl in agony.

Emma threw him a paper towel. *"Don't be such a baby, Matt. You're not dying! And besides, I'm going to win today so you didn't stand a chance anyways."*

Matt pulled himself together, glared at Sandra and made a menacing gesture toward her. *"You did that on purpose,"* he accused her.

Sandra looked blissfully innocent and stated that she couldn't imagine why Matt could possibly think she was capable of doing such a thing. Matt reluctantly joined Grant and the others on the desks in the centre of the room. With the paper towel he wiped his tears, blew his nose and then used it to mop up the blood on his arm.

Emma was already mounted and ready to go on her old Canadian Tire bike. It wasn't as flashy as the boys' bikes, in fact, it was a hand-me-down from her brother and had a crossbar like all boys' bikes. She had tried to make it distinctive by painting it green, but the only green paint they had at home was a sickly lime colour, so it really hadn't turned out the way she had envisioned. Emma wasn't one to dwell on such trivial issues as the colour of her bike, but she had had to endure much teasing from the boys at school. They called her bike "the lemon" or "slime" and generally made life miserable for her. Today was going to be her day of redemption. She would show those guys that it didn't matter what colour her bike was.

The boys started chanting, *"Lemon! Lemon! Lemon!"*

The girls tried to out yell them with, *"Emma! Emma! Emma!!"*

She flung her leg over the crossbar and waited for Janey to lower her arm. The signal came. *"Go!"*

Off Emma went, rounding each corner with finesse and making the turns with no spills. She was headed for the finish line.

"Teacher!" yelled Glenn, the lookout.

Emma skidded to a stop, fell off her green machine and hit her knee on the chain of the bike. More blood. She grabbed a towel and got her bike out of the way as everyone worked together to return the desks to their proper places. Emma, Matt and Grant quickly put their bikes outside on the bike stand and pretended to be occupied with a game of hopscotch.

As Miss McCrea approached, she noticed Emma's bloody knee and Matt's bloody elbow. *"What on earth happened to you two?"* she asked with concern.

"I fell playing hopscotch," replied Emma.

"I tripped over my lunch box," explained Matt.

Miss McCrea accepted their excuses and proceeded into the schoolroom where everything was back in place.

There were no visible signs of the competition that had just occurred.

Miss McCrea rang the handbell and the children lined up, boys in one line, girls in another. As Matt and Grant passed Emma she whispered to them, *"I'll get you next time for sure. Just you wait and see!"*

Things were never dull during noon hour at School Section No. 7.

What Will He Think Of Next

Matt was a rascal, a mischievous little devil who got into trouble every time he turned around. To his advantage, he had a beguiling smile and big blue, innocent eyes, but even those features didn't always save him from the deserved punishment for the many pranks he masterminded. His friends found it hard to say no to his hair-brained ideas, so his accomplices often ended up in trouble too.

The one-room schoolhouse they attended was nestled amongst lilac bushes. But it was within the shelter of the cedar trees, that bordered the schoolyard, where much of the mischief took place. Popular activities included making cedar needle cigarettes and exchanging a first kiss.

Like most days, Matt and his cronies found themselves unsupervised in the schoolhouse. What an ideal time to do a little exploring. Matt often wondered what was beyond the trap door in the ceiling of the old schoolhouse. Today was the day he was going to find out! Their teacher, Miss McCrea, had gone home for lunch. It was the custom in those days to leave the children unsupervised at the schoolhouse during the lunch hour.

With some help from his buddies, Glenn and Steve, they shoved several desks out of the way, leaving one directly under the trapdoor. They placed a chair on top of the desk, making it just the right height to reach the trapdoor. Since it was Matt's idea, he was the first one to climb up onto the chair, and aided by a big boost from Glenn, he disappeared into the unknown dark abyss of the attic. A flurry of dust and dirt fell onto the boys down below.

Matt quickly discovered he couldn't see a thing and called immediately for some light. At first, Matt's cronies were at a loss. What could they use? Then, Steve remembered where the caretaker kept a small tin can that contained matches that were used to fire up the pot-bellied stove. Time was now of the essence and they knew they were working against the clock; Miss McCrea would soon be returning from lunch.

Glenn, with matches in hand, joined Matt in the attic with Steve's help. Then Steve hopped up, using his unusually long arms to good advantage to maneuver himself up without assistance.

Simply using the matches gave them a brief and dim light. They needed something brighter and much more lasting to see what was up there. Some old newspapers on the attic floor seemed just the thing. They rolled the newspapers tightly together to make a flare, just as Matt had seen his dad do. It worked. They could see the entire attic. It was filled with broken desks, parts of chairs, Christmas decorations, an old flag and several paint cans. All of a sudden the tight roll of paper disappeared and the flames crept close to Matt's hands.

He yelled and dropped the burning paper, right on top of the pile of old newspapers.

"Water! Help! Someone get some water! The place is on fire!" Matt yelled. His screams provoked immediate action. Steve jumped from the attic, grabbed the pail of water they used for drinking and lifted it up to Matt, while most of the water spilled onto Steve's head!

"More water!" Matt screamed as he threw down the empty pail.

This time, Steve ran out to the pump in the yard and filled the pail. By now another student had arrived on the scene. George was much taller and stronger than Steve and was able to hold the pail up for Matt with little spillage. Luckily, that pailful of water was just enough to douse the fire. Only a lingering smell of burning paper and some steam rising from the sodden mess remained as a reminder of the whole event.

The boys made a hasty retreat from the attic. Miss McCrea would return at any minute. They opened the door of the schoolhouse and attempted to rid the classroom of the smoky smell resulting from the fire.

Miss McCrea returned from lunch, somewhat surprised, to a classroom of students who greeted her politely and quickly sat at their desks when she rang the bell for afternoon classes. Lucky for the culprits, that day, Miss McCrea was so stuffed up with a head cold, she couldn't smell a thing. She sat down at her desk and proceeded to read aloud the next chapter of a book, appropriately titled, *Cue For Treason.* This reading activity held the children spellbound every afternoon. After a few minutes of reading, little drops of water began to drip down on the teacher's desk. She looked up at the ceiling, puzzled at the leak. It hadn't rained recently and there didn't seem to be any explanation for the continuous dripping of water.

"I'll have to call the Chairman of the Board to look into this," she stated.

Matt didn't need any Chairman to tell him what it was. The only thoughts he had at the moment were related to what the Chairman of the Board would discover in the attic, the resulting inquiry that would ensue and the punishment that would be meted out for one more innocent prank that had been planned and carried out by Matt and his co-conspirators.

Matt's Favourite Smells Of Springtime

It was springtime once more in the country and it was the smells at this time of the year that Matt loved the most. His favourites included the smell of grass growing and the distinct fishy odour coming from the creek which sent him in search of his fishing pole in the basement. The creek was open with no chunks of ice left to impede the flow of water. It wouldn't be long before he would head out to the bay where the fish were plentiful.

It was also in the springtime that spring cleaning began in earnest. Mom opened all the windows to allow the spring breezes to flow freely through the house. She assigned Matt and Jenn the job of putting all of the rugs out on the clothesline to beat with sticks to rid them of the winter's accumulation of dust. When the rugs had been beaten clean, Jenn and Matt chased each other with the sticks, like frisky little calves let out to pasture.

It was in the early springtime too, over several weeks, that Matt and Jenn could not ride their bikes to school because the road was muddy, wet and full of deep ruts. And it was because of the wet conditions that Mom had to constantly remind them, *"Don't you dare get any soakers today!"* "Soakers" was the word she used for their soaked boots. Their boots would become so wet from one return trip from school that they would be barely dry enough to be worn the next day.

On this particular day that Matt and Jenn started off for school, Matt suggested they take a shortcut through the fields to cut off a twisty corner. This route would save them much time and it seemed like a good idea. So off they went, trudging through the wet pasture and climbing over fences when necessary. Finally, they came upon a long stretch of cedar rail fence that ran along Mr. Sadler's field. Always ready for a challenge, they mounted the fence and walked along the uppermost rails, struggling to maintain their balance. Jenn was the first to fall onto the wet, spongy field. Soaking wet, she blamed Matt for her mishap. Matt was quite used to being blamed for one thing or another but that didn't stop him from jumping off the fence and coming to Jenn's rescue. He brushed off the mud as much as possible and poured the water out of her rubber boots. He had no idea that the fields that he had decided to cross were so wet. It was at this moment that Jenn reminded him about Mom's warning regarding the soakers.

Matt just shrugged his shoulders and hurriedly led them away from this marshy area to dryer land and as he glanced back to ensure that Jenn was keeping up, *he* lost his balance and fell face first onto the wet, muddy soil. It was Jenn's turn to help him up and dump the water out of his boots. *"**Now**, do you remember what Mom said about not getting soakers?"*

Matt and Jenn finally arrived at school just as the bell rang. Their teacher, Miss McCrea, couldn't help but notice their condition—they were wet all the way through. Matt's woolly breeks were sodden, his boots made a squishing sound when he walked and his socks were wringing wet. Jenn, in much the same condition, was shivering from the damp cold.

At Miss McCrea's insistence, Jenn removed her wet socks and coat and hung them on a clothesline by the furnace to dry. There on the clothesline alongside Jenn's clothing were Matt's breeks and several other pairs of boys' pants, a testimony to the fact that many others had suffered the same fate! Jenn then wrapped herself in a big, dry blanket that Miss McCrea had given her. As Matt sat at his desk, he knew he was not alone. Many of the children sat at their desks, wearing only long underwear.

As everyone's steaming wet, woolly pants dried by the furnace, the room was filled with the odour of wet wool. This was one springtime odour that Matt did not relish!

Matt and Jenn hoped against hope that their clothes would be dry by home time. If they didn't arrive at home by the appointed hour, Mom and Dad would think that they had gotten a detention as a result of getting into trouble at school. This would mean double trouble: punishment at school, some explaining to do at home and possibly even more punishment.

During recess time that day, everyone who was in their long underwear had to stay inside and help the teacher wipe the morning's work from the blackboard, clean the brushes and fill the water pail. Those with dry clothing were allowed out to play. For those imprisoned inside the classroom, the sound of laughter coming from the fun and games outside made the recess seem longer than usual.

The afternoon passed slowly. Matt made sure the furnace was full of wood so the heat would dry their clothes by four o'clock. The amount of heat had everyone sweating and complaining about the unpleasant odour of drying clothes. Finally, Jenn's clothes were fit to wear.

The remaining pants and socks were still damp but dry enough to put on. Miss McCrea gave them a stern warning. *"All of you must go straight home and don't dilly dally at the bridge. Once home you must get out of your damp clothes so you don't catch a cold!"*

It was advice that Matt had every intention of keeping, that is, until they came to the bridge. It was at this place that he and Jenn would often toss stones at the wire fence nearby. Whoever hit the wire first would win the prize of dessert left over from the noon meal. They knew they shouldn't linger, but Matt's suggestion came easily and quickly. *"Let's throw stones for the dessert. It won't take long. I bet I can hit the wire with my first shot."*

"Bet you can't," Jenn quickly responded, and so the contest began.

Neither of them had any luck until the fifth attempt, when Matt pinged the stone off the wire first. Angry at losing the game, Jenn stamped her feet and threw her school bag at Matt. Matt ducked out of the way just at that moment and the school bag went over the bridge and landed by the edge of the creek. Jenn cried and wailed about her now drenched school bag. Matt, good-natured as ever, once more came to the rescue. Carefully he negotiated a descent down the bank of the creek, broke off a branch from a nearby bush, and with it, prodded the school bag close enough so he could grab a hold of it. However, in the process the creek water flowed over the top of his rubber boots—creating a couple more "soakers". *"Oh well, what's a little bit more water,"* he declared.

Finally, Matt and Jenn arrived home. Mom asked about their day and if they had managed to stay out of the water.

"We're just fine," said Jenn.

"Perfectly dry!" replied Matt.

When Mom returned to her work in the pantry, Matt and Jenn quickly retrieved their rubber boots and turned them upside down over the register to dry, hoping that Mom wouldn't inspect them more closely.

Matt then sat down and devoured a big bowl of tasty Johnny cake and maple syrup—another one of his favourite spring smells!

Auntie Kate and Uncle Billie

"The 'salt of the earth' is coming for supper," I said to my sister. She knew who I meant without any further explanation. Mother always referred to Auntie Kate and Uncle Billie as the "salt of the earth". And they were!

They lived in a small, log house on the hill just in back of our place in Lanark County. The ridge, on which their house was built, had a beautiful panoramic view of the valley below. The road to their place winded through some small hills and gullies until it reached its peak on top of the ridge. We called it "the million dollar view". Auntie Kate and Uncle Billie eked out a living on this stony land by raising a few cattle, a dozen hens and some pigs.

They were old, tiny and wizened. I never saw them dressed in anything but black, but in my imagination I believed that if they were robed in green they would look exactly like the mythical Irish leprechauns. Not only did they look like leprechauns, but they spoke with a broad Irish brogue that was said to be more Irish than the Irish themselves. They were very loving towards each other and often held hands when they sat side by side.

They weren't related to us, but it was a sign of respect to call them Auntie Kate and Uncle Billie. Everyone else in the community called them by the same names. On every visit, Auntie Kate took time to explain that she really wasn't our auntie, she was only our dad's third cousin once removed—whatever that meant! Often the neighbour kids called them the Hillbillies, but we always came to their defense.

This lovely spring Saturday, my sister and I watched for their buggy to come down the road. On clear days we could hear them before they actually came into view because Uncle Billie had sleigh bells on his buggy, summer *and* winter.

"The bells keep the horses awake!" was Uncle Billie's excuse for not removing them during the summer.

On this particular day, they arrived at our house and, as usual, drove around to the back door to unload Auntie Kate. It was always quite a procedure and we never wanted to miss it. Dad held the reins while Uncle Billie jumped out of the buggy. Like a little elf he scurried around to the back of the buggy, yelling, *"Stay put Katie. Stay put. I'll get ye down my luv!"*

Now, Uncle Billie must have weighed 110 pounds soaking wet and even though Auntie Kate was short, she had a considerable girth. There was no way he could have supported her bulk if she had landed on him. I guess that's the possibility we were waiting for—there was always the outside chance that we would witness him getting flattened. In his squeaky, high pitched voice he kept reminding Auntie Kate that he was on his way to help her. *"Stay put, Katie! Stay put!"*

Well, the poor woman had no choice. She couldn't manage taking the steps down from the buggy on her own, partly because the distance between them was much too great for her stubby, wee legs and partly because she couldn't see them—her long, black skirt hid them entirely. For support, she leaned on the side of the buggy which then took on a severe list like a sinking ship. Uncle Billie stretched his arms out to her to help her down the steps for further support. My dad always positioned himself directly behind Uncle Billie in case he went down in the process.

I often visualized the three of them all falling backwards in a heap—similar to what you see in a slapstick movie—with Auntie Kate on top, kicking her little legs like an eggbeater. Of course that never happened, but I had a fertile imagination and was always ready for the possibilities!

Our procession then made its way into the kitchen where the table was set and the meal was ready for our guests. Auntie Kate always came with a brown paper bag clutched in her hand and this day was no exception. It was her version of a hostess gift and one never knew what the bag might contain. Sometimes it contained some eggs, or a bottle of jam, a homemade dish towel or some other item from their farm. My sister and I waited in anticipation, but she didn't present the bag to my mom. Oh well, we thought, she'd do it later. They were seated at the table next to the wall because that's where guests always sat. That meant that the rest of us could easily get up from the table to help serve and clean up. Auntie Kate and Uncle Billie would remain there for the duration of their visit. Farm people always visited in the kitchen and these two, once settled in, weren't very portable.

No matter what Mom served, it was always greeted with, *"Oh this is lovely darlin'!"*

The meal passed without incident. Auntie Kate and Uncle Billie got caught up with the local news, with both of them often talking at the same time. It was a cacophony of chatter and virtually impossible to listen to and make sense of the various conversations happening at the same time. When they had finished eating, they sat and held hands as they raved about the meal and complimented the cook.

"It was just lovely, darlin'." They repeated.

Still the brown paper bag was not presented.

Finally, their visit had come to an end and after hugs and thanks from them they went outside. Dad had brought their team and buggy around to the back steps and the mounting process began. Uncle Billie hoisted Auntie Kate into the buggy by shoving her from behind, in spite of her constant protestations. When she was safely in place he ran around and hopped up onto the driver's side. They were all set to go. They turned out of our driveway, waving goodbye and thanking us again. As they disappeared down the road and over the hill, Auntie Kate was looking back and still waving goodbye with both hands. But where was the brown paper bag?

We went into the house to look for it and help clean up. There it was on the floor right beside their chairs. My sister and I dived for it and looked inside. *What was this?* The bag was full of chicken feathers and the neck and legs of a freshly plucked chicken! What a strange gift. It remained a mystery for several days until Auntie Kate telephoned Mom to thank her for the visit.

"How did you enjoy the chicken we brought you?" Auntie Kate asked.

Mom quickly collected her thoughts and stammered, *"It was really good,"* and thanked Auntie Kate for her kindness.

"We plucked it especially for you darlin'," Auntie Kate replied.

We never found out the truth about the gift. We deduced that "the salt of the earth" had killed, plucked and cleaned a chicken for us and put it in a brown paper bag to bring to our house, but instead they had mistakenly put it in the garbage. Then, they had put the feathers, neck and legs into another similar bag and brought it to us. We were the losers in that deal!

Irene's Bloomers

It was 1942 and the war impacted on everyone's life, including the lives of those who lived in Lanark County in the Ottawa Valley. Money was scarce and the decent thing to do was not to complain about the lack of commodities. Farm folk were very resilient and neighbours came to the rescue when needed. If sugar was scarce at Irene's house, her mother knew she could borrow some from the Scotts next door. Everyone was in the same predicament and people learned to endure the frugal lifestyle.

That was all fine with Irene, a very determined ten-year-old. She could put up with most things. She didn't mind the long walk to and from school. It was a normal part of Irene's day, just the way that bus rides are a part of a student's routine today. Everyone knows the old story: *"I had to walk to school through snow drifts up to my waist, uphill all the way, in my father's pyjamas."* In reality it wasn't quite that severe! Irene didn't wear her father's pyjamas, she often got rides to school and the road was as flat as the prairies. It wasn't the walk that presented a problem for her. In fact, she rather enjoyed having some thinking time while walking.

But there was a problem that consumed her. It was her underwear. It was a delicate situation, and she feared it would scar her for life. This is what ate up Irene's thoughts during the long walk to school and the equally long journey home: she imagined all kinds of embarrassing scenarios concerning her underwear that was made from old bleached Redpath Sugar bags.

"I hate this underwear," Irene complained to her mother.

"It's perfectly fine. It's warm and it's clean and all the other girls are wearing the same thing," that was Mother's ready response. Mother did her best to convince Irene that flour bags were perfectly acceptable and that everyone wore the same thing—maybe a different brand—but all the mothers sewed underwear and bed linens by reusing the same coarse, bleached cotton. How could her mother be sure, though, what the other girls wore for underwear?

Irene realized that the subject of having to wear recycled cotton bags had little room for negotiation, but she still tried. *"But I can still see the words Redpath Sugar, and if I can see them, I bet you everyone else can too,"* wailed Irene.

"If you behave like a lady, no one will see your underwear," Mother replied emphatically. She knew what a tomboy Irene was and that the tallest tree or the roughest game was no deterrent for her untamed daughter.

Mother concluded that Irene was exaggerating about the lettering on her underwear. She had washed and bleached those sugar bags four or five times and was certain that no red words were visible. At least not unless you looked *really* closely. In these tough war years, it would be a sin to waste such good cotton material like that and not reuse it for something. She had to admit to herself, though, that she really did understand how Irene felt about having to wear recycled sugar bags but things were pretty tight at home just now. If only this dreadful war would end and things could get back to normal. Then, she promised herself, she would buy some pretty, frilly underwear with lace for Irene.

Irene couldn't help it, but she felt like she was the only one who had to wear these awful bloomers. This thought perhaps bothered her even more than the fact that she wore them. What did the other girls wear? It was a very personal subject and she wasn't too sure how it could be approached. She knew she couldn't casually ask someone what their underwear was like, but the temptation was certainly there.

Irene knew one thing for sure, that snobby Mary Jane Potts had lace on her bloomers. She knew it for a fact. And how did she know? Well, Mary Jane made many trips to the teacher's desk during the school day and she did it only to "brown nose" so she could be Miss McCrea's pet. Well, one day, as Mary Jane approached Miss McCrea's desk for the umpteenth time, Irene just happened to stick out her foot. Mary Jane fell and blushed a deep red as she gave Irene a hateful glare. She tried modestly to pull her skirt around her knees, but she wasn't fast enough. Irene caught a glimpse of pink lace at the bottom of white bloomers. White bloomers! White bloomers with no red printing. And pink lace too. What a luxury! How she envied Mary Jane. She even hated her for that lace.

That flash of pink lace ruined the day for Irene, but it also gave her a mission in life. One day, she was going to have pretty underwear with lace if it was the last thing she did on this earth.

When Irene got home from school that day, Mother had an errand for her. She asked her to walk the half mile to Mary Jane's house to return the Eaton's Catalogue that Mother had borrowed from Mrs. Potts.

Oh no! That was the last place she wanted to go, considering the events of the day. It was futile to argue with Mother. No amount of pleading and promises to do other errands would get her out of this predicament. Resigned to this horrible task she went on her way, hoping it would be a quick trip with no contact with Mary Jane. She was wrong.

Mary Jane and her mother were in the yard by the clothesline, bringing in the wash. Mrs. Potts greeted Irene with a friendly smile. *"Hello Irene. I see you brought back the catalogue. Thanks for doing that. Will you stay for a glass of lemonade?"*

"Thank-you, but I better get back home," replied Irene never taking her eyes off of Mary Jane.

Mary Jane ignored Irene and quickly continued to grab the clothes off the line, almost as if she were trying to hide something. Mrs. Potts continued to chat. Irene suddenly realized that the clothes that Mary Jane was removing from the line were several pairs of bloomers, made from white bleached cotton and there was no pink lace on any of them! There they were, big as life itself, three pairs of bloomers with red lettering spelling Redpath Sugar and one pair with blue lettering that spelled Purity Flour. Irene couldn't take her eyes off this wonderful sight. Oh sweet day! She could never thank her mother enough for asking her to take the Eaton's catalogue back to Mary Jane's mother.

Even snobby Mary Jane wore Redpath Sugar bag bloomers! And Mother did a far better bleaching job on Irene's bloomers than Mrs. Potts did on Mary Jane's. There *really* was no comparison. It appeared that Mary Jane had only one pair of bloomers with lace and Irene could easily live with that. It was a wonderful day indeed to discover that Miss Snobby Mary Jane had to endure the red lettering of Redpath Sugar and the blue of Purity Flour!

Paddy's Christmas

Patrick James Joyce O'Brien was three and a half years old the Christmas of 1962. Everyone called him Paddy except when he was being reprimanded by his mother. Then, she called him by his full name with her strong Irish brogue accent—*Patrick James Joyce O'Brien*—making it sound particularly ominous!

Paddy was full of wide-eyed wonderment at all the customs surrounding the Christmas season. He was the youngest of four children and this year, for the first time, he was considered old enough to accompany the others to the bush across the fields from his house to chop down an evergreen tree. It never occurred to the family to ask permission from the owner of the bush to actually cut the tree down. But, how could it not be fine with the owner, Tom McGee? It also never occurred to Paddy's family to wonder at the wisdom of sending four children into the forest with an axe. That's the way it was always done in those days.

The first thing this troupe of four did was to locate the best tree, agree that it was the best tree and then visualize what it would look like in their living room.

Jack, the oldest and the keeper of the axe, had learned from past mistakes to make a complete assessment of the situation. Two years ago they had dragged home the most beautiful scotch pine tree that they could find, but to their disappointment it wouldn't fit into the living room. They had to chop away at it until only a skeleton of the formerly gorgeous tree remained. With this in mind they began their search.

"There's a good one!" shouted Paddy to the others.

"That one's no good," said Lila, *"it only has one decent side."*

After rejecting all of Paddy's suggestions, they finally found the right one.

"What kind of a tree is it?" Paddy inquired.

Jack liked to show off his knowledge about nature, so he replied to his little brother, *"Take one of the needles in between your fingers. If it spins easily, it's a spruce. If it balks at spinning it's a balsam. Spruce spins, and balsam balks!"* Paddy tried it and announced that their Christmas tree this year was a spruce.

With a great show of strength, Jack chopped the tree down and the four headed back home dragging the spruce behind them. Paddy, with his short little legs, found it tiring to walk in the snow and soon chanced upon a free ride by lying down on the tree as Jack dragged it across the fields.

Back home, Mother and Dad O'Brien admired the children's choice and were soon busy setting it up in the living room. That same night was the night for the Christmas concert, so Paddy was ordered to bed for a nap, as it was his responsibility to do the welcome recitation for the concert. As he lay down, he relived his first Christmas tree cutting excursion and practiced the welcome recitation. He knew it off by heart.

"Some folks get the measles
Some folks get the flu
I've got Christmas spirit
I hope you get it too."

He drifted off to sleep with those words on his lips. The next thing he knew, Lila was shaking him awake. *"Get up sleepy head. It's supper time!"*

Paddy had trouble concentrating on supper as he could hardly bear the excitement of appearing on stage–all by himself—and in front of all those people .

The concert was held in the little community hall in the village. Lit only by three ceiling lights it was quite dark inside, giving the hall a Christmasy atmosphere. A big, black pot-bellied stove stood in the middle, heating the room. Stove pipes reached up to the ceiling and over to the chimney. Where should one sit? If you were near the stove, you'd roast. If you were too far away, you'd freeze. It was a difficult decision to make.

Extra chairs had been brought in from the church and the older Sunday School children had made decorations. The usually dark, dingy walls had been transformed for the occasion with green garlands and popcorn chains; candy canes hung between each loop made by the garlands and chains. Paddy found the candy cane that he had created and excitedly pointed it out to his mom. It was easy to identify Paddy's; his was purple and white while all the others were red and white. Paddy was particularly fond of purple.

The best and most responsible job of the evening was given to four children who were ten and older—they were the *Curtain Pullers*. The job was in such demand that the Sunday School Superintendent had to choose the children to share the task. Two were chosen for the first half of the concert and the other two were chosen for the second half. Pulling the curtain for the last half of the concert carried much more prestige, because it was from behind that curtain, at the very end of the concert, that Santa would appear. The *Curtain Pullers* were warned by the Superintendent. *"Now don't you be peeking out from behind the curtains."* She might as well have been talking to the wind, because that's exactly what they did. They peeked out from the sides and they even peeked out from underneath the curtains to wave to their friends!

The program began with a "few words" from the minister. It seemed that Reverend Armstrong didn't understand what "a few" meant. Paddy knew that after the Reverend had spoken, he was on stage next. His nervousness grew as he waited for the minister to finish. He quickly went over the recitation in his head, *"Some folks get the measles, some folks get the flu. I've got Christmas spirit, I hope you get it too."* There! He knew it all right!

There was a polite applause after the minister finally finished his "few words". Paddy heard his name being announced for the welcome recitation. He mounted the stage, went behind the curtain, placed himself in exactly the middle of the stage and waited for the curtain to be drawn. Paddy looked stunning in his shiny shoes, black pants, white shirt and purple bow tie that Mom had made for him. Paddy knew he looked good too, so he swelled out his chest and began his recitation in a big, loud voice, just the way he had practiced. Loud enough too, so the old folks could hear.

He made his bow and began.

"Some folks get the measles.
Some folks get the flu.
I hope you get it too."

There was brief pause, a few titters and then the applause came. Oh, it felt wonderful. He bowed again and strutted off the stage into his mom's arms. She gave him a big hug and told him she was proud of him.

He never did find out that he had left out the crucial third line. It didn't matter. He had enjoyed his brief time of fame in the spotlight. And he looked so good! Maybe some day he would be asked to be a *Curtain Puller*.

Kindergarten Christmas Concert: The Potential for Peril

It was the evening of the annual kindergarten Christmas Concert. Every sibling, parent, grandparent and favourite auntie and uncle would soon crowd into the school gym for the event. It was the highlight of the year. The children had practised seriously for two weeks and they seemed to be prepared, but apprehension lingered in Miss West's mind as she put on her best dress for the event. She felt the potential for peril. It was going to be one of those nights—she could feel it in her bones.

The walls were decorated with seasonal art work prepared by the children. Full-size silhouettes of each student graced the back wall. Each student had coloured their own art work and most of them were quite attractive. Then there was Jimmy's. He had all the features in the right place, but he had added an extra eye. The three eye balls were placed in such a way that it made him appear to look like a cross-eyed Cyclopes. But that was the way he wanted it and Miss West had not wanted to change his mind. She comforted herself with the rationalization that because she hadn't squelched his creativity, perhaps, some day, he would become a famous science fiction illustrator.

Miss West arrived at the school at 6:00 p.m. to give the final inspection to the gym and props for the evening program. The children had baked fourteen loaves of raisin bread and made dozens of decorated sugar cookies for the snack at the end of the concert. She proceeded to slice the loaves of bread, butter them and placed them on trays.

The phone rang. It was a parent checking on the correct time for the concert. When she returned to buttering the bread, she was horrified to see the classroom pet rabbit, Bunny, chewing on a loaf of raisin bread.

"Shoo!" she screamed and the brazen rabbit dropped the loaf and scurried back to its cage. Someone had left the cage door open and Bunny had taken full advantage of the opportunity to have a snack. Miss West pitched the chewed loaf into the waste basket, finished her task and placed the prepared trays up high out of the reach of children and pets! Would that dreaded feeling in her bones continue to materialize? This had been event number one—hopefully the last!

Finally, all the children had been dropped off at the kindergarten room. The parents proceeded to the gym where they vied for the best seats. Many had movie cameras and were busy getting them aimed and focused at the stage.

All the children were dressed in their Sunday best. Miss West glowed with pride. Jimmy, as well as being artistic, had strong organizational skills; he used those skills now to get the children lined up to parade into the gym. So far so good, Miss West thought to herself, if the Bunny incident was to be the only incident, she could live with that. Maybe her premonition for disaster was ill founded. She tried to think positively!

As they proceeded to the gym, two policemen met Miss West in the hall and explained that they had accompanied the father of one of her students from prison so he could see her perform at the concert. There was a restraining order that prevented the father from seeing Sally alone. Sally, upon seeing her dad, broke rank and ran to him, giving him a big hug. He held her tightly for a few minutes as the children stood open mouthed. When this strange meeting had ended, the children, in awe of the policemen, waved and smiled at them as they continued on their way to the stage. The police and their squad car would remain for the whole concert, and afterwards, with haste, they would sweep Sally's dad back to prison. That was event number two!

Miss West proceeded to the piano, situated on the gym floor below the stage, where she supplied the music for the singing that would soon begin. The children had all gathered in their proper order on the stage behind the curtain. They were ready for their opening chorus. Several of the children in the front row peeked under the curtain, found their parents and waved happily. Others, spread the curtains apart in the middle of the stage and called to their moms and dads.

Finally, Jimmy stuck his head out from behind the curtain and announced, *"Everything's A-okay up here Miss West!"* The audience shuffled and tittered, releasing some built-up tension.

The first part of the program went very well and included several Christmas songs. Sally had the solo part in the song, *Who Has a Beard That's Snowy White?* She sang like an angel and Miss West knew that she was singing for her dad.

The next item was a dramatization of the Christmas Story. Everyone got into their costumes with a minimum of shoving and pushing and very few tears. Miss West narrated the old story of Jesus's birth with the children adding some dialogue. Miss West continued her recitation, *"Mary and Joseph had to leave their home in Nazareth to go to Bethlehem to be counted. They bundled up some belongings and left their house."*

As she finished this part, Judy, who was playing the part of Mary, poked Steve, who was playing Joseph and said to him, *"Lock the door dummy!"* This part was not in the script! Miss West valiantly carried on in spite of the extra dialogue.

Cameras flashed and the dramatization proceeded. The shepherds made their way to the manger with a toy lamb. Suddenly a full-fledged fight took place between shepherd number one and shepherd number two. They each wanted to present the lamb to Mary. The shepherds tugged at the fuzzy toy almost tearing it from limb to limb. Finally, Joseph took control, retrieved the lamb and placed it in the manger. The two shepherds glared at each other and sulked. So ended events number three and four.

The kings were the next ones to enter. Miss West played some Eastern sounding music for the kingly procession. The three regally dressed Magi marched solemnly up the centre aisle of the gym as the music played. All of a sudden the first king gave a shout, *"Jeese, I forgot the gold!"* He tore out of the gym, raced to the classroom, got the gold covered box and returned to his place in the procession. That was event number five, and hopefully the last glitch.

The next item on the program was a dramatization of the story, *The Elves and the Shoemaker*. Harry was the narrator, a very bright boy who knew the whole story off by heart. Miss West was confident that this would proceed with no problem. Harry was a little timid as he started his narration, but gained confidence with every word. Suddenly Harry stopped reciting and exclaimed, *"Oh, Oh."* He stood there frozen in time, as a small puddle appeared on the floor at his feet. He had wet his pants and was obviously very embarrassed. Mrs. Moore, who was helping with the children, gathered Harry in her arms and rushed him back to the classroom to get a fresh pair of pants.

Jimmy waved his hand and snapped his fingers at Miss West, shouting out, *"I can do Harry's part. I know it—really I do!"* Jimmy took over the narration until Harry returned with fresh, clean pants and with an eagerness to take his rightful place back on stage. Jimmy reluctantly allowed him to carry on. Event number six!

It was time for the last item on the program. Santa arrived, sat each child on his knee and offered every one of them a small gift. When Santa had finished with the gift giving, he gave Miss West a big hug and wished everybody a Merry Christmas! Miss West could detect the distinct odour of whiskey on Santa's breath and hoped he would make a quick exit before he encountered any parents! Event number seven!

At the end of the concert, as the parents snacked on the raisin bread and cookies, there was a marked feeling of joy and pride in the gym. After collecting their children, no one failed to congratulate Miss West on the wonderful concert.

Afterwards, when Miss West and Mrs. Moore were left to clean up the wrapping paper, the mess and the puddle on the stage, Miss West breathed a sigh of relief, *"I'm glad that's over. This is definitely the last Christmas Concert I'm doing. It's just too much work and a whole lot of stress!"* But deep in her heart Miss West knew she would go through it all again next Christmas, despite the potential for peril!

Alice and Dorothy Cull the Hens

Alice, Dorothy and little Joan waved goodbye as the '41 Chevy, carrying Mom and Dad Lowry, disappeared around the corner and out of view. They had mixed feelings about their parents leaving: feelings of freedom, feelings of apprehension, all combined with a tinge of loneliness. The three children were on their own for a month to run the family farm until their parents returned. It really was a good thing that Alice and Dorothy were fearless and little Joan really didn't understand what was happening!

It was springtime. The crops were in and the hay wasn't ready to be cut, so Mom and Dad Lowry had decided to take a month-long trip out West to the prairies. They trusted the old '41 Chevy to do the job and make it out to Saskatchewan. Once there, they planned to visit some long-lost relatives to whom they had written to say that they were coming. As yet they hadn't received a reply. *"Oh well, we'll go anyway,"* said Dad. *"We'll find someone to visit and we'll have a good look at the scenery."* He wasn't much on details and would never have thought of phoning to confirm their visit.

A local neighbour lady, Mrs. Boal, had agreed to stay the month with the girls and help look after five-year-old Joan, but the farming operation was to be trusted to the girls. Mom and Dad thought that they would get along just fine.

Alice, 16 years of age and Dorothy 15 years of age, as well as looking after the cows, the hens and a couple of pigs, had to attend school. Right from the get-go, it was a mad rush in the morning: they had to get the chores done, get washed and dressed and be ready for the school bus. Often the school bus driver would see them running for the bus with their coats half on, one hand grasping a piece of toast and the other waving goodbye to little Joan. The bus driver always waited patiently and admired their feisty natures.

While her sisters were at school, Joan loved to play in the sand box. She mixed the water and sand, making fancy castles to show her sisters on their return. One day she made a particularly beautiful castle with several turrets. She was so proud of it she stood back to admire her work. All of a sudden she heard a noise. One of the pigs had escaped from the pig pen and was running straight for her beloved, beautiful castle. She tried to shoo it away by yelling and waving her hands. That didn't work. The wild beast was headed on a direct path towards her work of art. She ran at the pig, fell on top of it, held on and went for a brief ride on its back, screaming all the while. Mrs. Boal, hearing the ruckus, ran to investigate the problem. Joan was still lying over the back of the pig, so Mrs. Boal grabbed her apron and whooshed it up and down to distract the animal. Joan fell off, the pig detoured around the sandbox and Mrs. Boal rescued a crying Joan.

Together, Mrs. Boal and Joan cornered the pig and got it back into its pen. Joan had acquired several scrapes on her arms and knees. Just at that moment the school bus arrived with Dorothy and Alice. They immedidately learned about the whole story from Joan, in between sobs. Alice comforted her little sister while Dorothy went to the barn and returned with a can of salve.

"Here, let me put this udder balm on your cuts. It's good for cuts that the cows get on their udders, so it should help your scrapes," Dorothy said as she slathered a goodly amount of salve on the wounds. Finally, Joan recovered enough to show off her still intact castle.

The following Saturday, Alice asked a neighbour to take her to town so she could get some groceries. Dad had left $100.00 in a tea can to last them the month. They felt like millionaires! Once at the grocery store, Alice bought a couple of loaves of bread, peanut butter and few other items. She also bought some penny candy as a treat for Joan. While she was at the cash register, waiting to pay for her goods, she gasped in shock at the lady in front of her as she paid for her groceries. Her total came to $12.45. Alice couldn't imagine anyone spending that much on food!

Back at the farm, the girls managed the chores, tended the garden and even got their homework done every night. As members of the softball team, they continued their games and even practiced for the upcoming track meet, as they were star athletes at their high school. Alice decided that they needed a sand pit at home to practice the broad and long jump to fine tune their skills. With the old, pointed shovel in hand, Alice started to dig in a soft spot in the garden. Little Joan came to see what was going on, realized what Alice was doing, disappeared on the run and returned with her little sandbox shovel and started to dig alongside Alice. It took a few days but with persistence the pit was ready. They then sprinkled it with sawdust from the shed—it almost looked like a real broad jump pit. Every night the girls worked on their jumping skills and even Joan was given a turn. After all she had been a digger.

Being conscientious about looking after the farm, Alice one day realized that the hens weren't laying as many eggs as they should. She checked their food and water—both were in good supply. What was wrong? Mrs. Boal explained that sometimes when hens stopped laying, it meant their time was up, it was time to get rid of them. Little did she think that the girls would act on this bit of information. But they did and quickly! Alice called their Uncle Jack and told him she wanted to cull some hens but didn't know how to do it.

"Oh, your dad will look after that when he gets home," he responded.

That didn't suit these independent young women. Dorothy and Alice went over the hen problem once more and decided to call Uncle Jack again. *"We want to do the culling now and get rid of the hens that aren't laying. Will you come and show us how?"*

Their pleading was so convincing that he relented and said he'd be there on Saturday morning at nine o'clock. When he arrived, the girls' first question was, *"Where are your culling tools?"*

Uncle Jack held up his three middle fingers and said, *"This is all we need."* He then proceeded to teach the girls the fine art of hen culling. "*You catch the hens and bring them to me,"* he said. He then held the hen tightly upside down under his arm and placed his three fingers on the hen's "egg-laying orifice". He was too polite to explain any further about the place where the eggs came from! If the opening was three fingers wide, the hen was still laying and it was returned to the henhouse. If the opening was less than three fingers, the hen was not a layer so it was placed in another shed. Thus, the culling proceeded. They had great fun with Uncle Jack during this process. They joked and laughed and he thought it was wonderful that these two young girls would do such a thing. He would tease them for years to come about their hen adventure.

The girls became very adept at the process and soon had 40 hens that they found to be non-layers. Too bad for those slackers, because they would be sent to the hen man. The 40 non-producers were kept separately, awaiting their fate. The layers were returned to their shed to live and lay some more. Alice had decided to call Mr. Platt, the hen man, to come and pick up the culled hens. They went to bed that night pleased as punch with the hen culling operation and proud that they were able to carry on the farm work in their dad's absence.

The next morning, when they went to do the chores, they had a surprise. Their hard work of the previous day was for nought. All the hens were back together again—one big happy family. What had happened? They discovered that the fence separating the two groups of hens had a gaping hole in it and the non-layers hadn't wasted an opportunity to join the "producers". Lesser women would have broken down into sobs but not these two. They were angry, yes, but these stupid fowl were not going to outsmart them!

Dorothy and Alice now considered themselves experts on hen culling even though Dorothy despised hens—always had and always will. Begrudgingly, they went through the same process once more, this time, without Uncle Jack's help, and of course after the hole in the fence had been repaired. They had the hens ready for Mr. Platt when he arrived. This time they had 44 hens deemed as useless. The culling bar had been raised—most likely because vengeance was in the air!

The days passed quickly with no further incidents. Frequent letters from their parents were welcome and encouraging. They were very happy to know that their mom and dad were enjoying a well-deserved holiday.

One day the old '41 Chevy drove into the laneway with the horn tooting and arms waving out the windows. Mom and Dad were finally back. The three girls and Mrs. Boal ran out to meet them with hugs and kisses. A sense of relief spread over every one of them.

Dad went out and toured the barn to check things out. *"We seem to have lost a few hens. Did they get away on you?"*

They explained the need for culling the hens and showed Dad the money they had received from Mr. Platt for the lazy hens. Dad then mentioned the sawdust pit in the garden that he had noticed. They described how they had needed a sand pit to practice for the track meet. Dad seemed to breathe a sigh of relief. *"Oh,"* he sighed, *"I thought that maybe a cow had died and you buried her in the garden!"*

The girls were so glad to have their parents home that they didn't go to the barn for a whole week. The story of the hen culling got around and every time the girls saw Uncle Jack he would give them the three finger salute and a big wink!

Romance

The timing couldn't have been worse. Anna must have been out of her mind to break up with Jake. The decision to terminate their relationship was the right one, but why had she not looked at the calendar before she sent him on his way? The college prom was only two weeks away and here she was with a lovely, flouncy tulle dress and no date.

Jake had been Anna's boyfriend for the past year and in her mind he had grown a bit stale. Anna just couldn't envision spending her adult life talking about the beauty of the fins on a '56 Plymouth. Not only that, but one of their few big dates last summer had been a visit to the annual 12th of July Orange Parade. Whoopee! That parade and few other lack-lustre occasions had been the highlights of a whole year of steady dating.

After listening to the other girls talking about their boyfriends, she gathered that there was more to romance than what she and Jake shared. They always sounded so excited about their dates. Anna did a checklist of the pluses and minuses of her relationship with Jake. He definitely registered on the minus side, in fact, he received a passing grade in only a few areas.

In Jake's favour, he did drive a nifty car and Anna knew enough about differentials, Hollywood mufflers, brake linings and other things to carry on a meaningful discussion with him. But on the minus side, cars were his favourite and *only* topic of conversation! Perhaps her knowledge of cars is what had brought Anna and Jake together in the first place. Because Anna lived on a farm and had helped her dad repair many vehicles, she had a good baseline knowledge of engines. There is, however, a limit to the number of conversations one can engage in regarding the features of General Motors products versus those of Ford.

Another plus for Jake was that he held a steady job and could afford to take her to the occasional movie and on special occasions to the Sweet Shoppe for a butterscotch sundae. As well, he was polite to her parents and had great hair.

Now, on the minus side, and particularly on the all-important, 10-point kissing scale he barely scored a mediocre seven. Anna wanted the perfect 10 to enter her life!

Finally, Anna delivered the break-up news to Jake. He took it like a man, which actually disappointed Anna. She had envisioned a degree of protest, some begging and maybe even some whining. She had even prepared a line of defense regarding her decision, but she didn't get a chance to use it!

A few days later she discovered the reason for his easy acceptance of the break up. She saw him with a cute redhead who was hanging onto his arm at the local Auto Trade Show. They were both looking with great interest at the engine of a '60 Plymouth. Well, she thought to herself, her most sincere wish for Jake and the redhead was "happy motoring". She was actually secretly jealous and muttered to herself, *"I bet she doesn't even know a drive shaft from a muffler."*

Although she would never admit it, she was angry that Jake had found a soulmate so quickly. And here she was with a beautiful tulle dress and no dance partner for the prom! Time was marching on.

She had much work to do to find a date for the prom which was now only two weeks away. Fortunately, exams were over and she could afford to spend time devising strategies for meeting someone new. It was tricky getting back into circulation, but the motivation was right there hanging in her closet.

A good friend of Anna's finally agreed to set up a blind date with her and Steve, a local farm boy known as the Hunk. Their first date was a movie. In Anna's eyes the evening was a great success. She laughed, teased, flirted and didn't spend one minute talking about cars or any part of them.

When the evening came to an end, Anna's date accompanied her to the door to say good night. She had a plan of action. She had decided to demurely turn her cheek and refuse his good night kiss, hoping to impress him with her high, moral standards. She had even practiced batting her eyelashes the way Lana Turner did in the movie they had just seen. She didn't even get a chance to carry out her plan! Steve—Mr. Hunk—thanked her for the evening and said it had been a fun night. No attempt at a kiss! No promise of another date! Not even a wee hug! Steve ran to his car and sped away; all her hopes and dreams were shattered in 10 seconds flat.

She quickly escaped upstairs before anyone could ask her about her date. Angry and hurt, she stomped around her room, venting her frustration at her stuffed animals and kicking a few pairs of shoes around the room. She put on her pretty tulle dress and wore it to bed that night. She decided that this might be the only use she would get out of it as the prospects for finding a partner for the prom were starting to fade fast.

With the dawn of a new day breaking, Anna felt a renewal of hope. She was able to look at the previous night with new objectivity. She reviewed it, weighing its pluses and minuses. There were many positive aspects she recalled from her date with Steve; they had laughed, talked about friends they had in common and appeared to have the same taste in music. She had also spent far more time looking into Steve's gorgeous, baby blue eyes than analyzing his dry, unruly, curly locks, which definitely needed a good wash and some mousse to get them into shape. In the final analysis there were really only two negative aspects worth mentioning: no kiss and no second date. Steve, the Hunk, had fared far better on the first test than Jake had scored during the whole year.

The week passed with no further contact with the Hunk. Her hopes of a prom date diminished daily. Her mom became concerned and made weird suggestions such as, *"Why don't you let your brother take you to the prom. It would be a shame to stay at home when you have that lovely dress."*

Her brother? Now wouldn't that just be the living end! Didn't her mom realize how embarrassing that would be? One day her mom even suggested that Anna's older sister's boyfriend would be glad to escort her. Really! How desperate did her mom think she was? Well, come to think of it, she had just about reached that degree of desperation.

With exactly six days left until the prom, she decided to take the bull by the horns. That was her dad's favourite expression, and it seemed fitting for this occasion. She swallowed her pride, picked up the phone and called the Hunk. Anna explained that she was looking for a prom date and wondered if he was interested. She tried not to sound as if she were groveling. He wasn't ecstatic about the idea of going to the prom but was politely compliant. What a relief!

The prom dance was everything she could have hoped for. She was a vision in tulle, and Steve was dashing in gray pants and a navy jacket. The corsage was acceptable but not great. The music was upbeat and Steve was an unbelievable dancer. They whirled and twirled around the dance floor in a blur of flouncy tulle. His hair was an unruly mass of curls, with no mousse, but she could live with that because of the unexpected thing that happened.

At the end of the evening when he walked her to the door, he kissed her. It was a wonderful kiss—the ultimate! This was exactly what she had been looking for—the perfect 10 and real romance to enter her life.

Irma's Fall From Grace

Irma had a beautiful view from her kitchen window. It looked out on a panorama of trees and fields with a winding country road at the end of her lane. She called it her million dollar view. There was only one thing spoiling the scenery. Burdocks!

The burdocks were flourishing near the new flower bed at the bottom of her lane. Normally a few delinquent weeds wouldn't cause grief to this senior citizen and her philosophy was, after all, "live and let live". But in this case, what disturbed her was the fact that they were in plain view for all of her friends and neighbours to see as they drove by her laneway. She needed to do something about it.

The Whipper Snipper was her tool of choice to rid herself of the weeds. She hauled it out of the garage where it spent most of its time. There was one small problem, however, the Whipper Snipper had to be plugged into an electrical outlet at the house, which was a good distance from the bottom of the lane where the delinquent weeds grew. As in many other instances that required her resourcefulness, this situation really posed no difficulty for this ingenious senior.

She had solved greater dilemmas than this one. For example, there was the time she tried to put bird seed into a feeder that was too high for her short stature. She had set a bucket upside down and then attempted to stand on it to reach the feeder. Thinking that the bucket probably wasn't strong enough for her full weight, she stood on it with one foot only, guessing that she was placing only half her weight on the bucket! It didn't work out that way, as she soon discovered, when her foot went through the bucket! Undaunted, she continued to consider the problem as she attended to her injured leg. She decided that three buckets together would certainly strengthen the base and distribute her weight evenly. It worked! They held her securely until the feeder was full.

Irma's thoughts returned to the problem at hand. She realized that to solve it she needed several extension cords to reach the dreaded burdocks. She took one extension cord from each of the following items: the vacuum cleaner, the hair dryer, the toaster, the computer, the television and one last one from the Christmas tree lights that were stored in the basement. She then did a rough calculation of the total length of her cords and compared it to the approximate distance to the flower bed. It seemed that it would work. Down the lane she went with the Whipper Snipper in hand and the electrical cords trailing behind her. She hooked up the last cord. But there was no electric current! Perhaps she had tugged too hard, causing the cord at the house to become unplugged. Up the lane she walked, re-plugged the cord into the house and trudged back down the lane to tackle the burdocks.

By this time she was starting to feel somewhat frustrated by the whole operation. A fleeting thought went through her head: *"Maybe I could live with those stupid burdocks!"* Yet, she wasn't quite ready to give up. She stretched the cord to its full length and discovered that her math calculations were in error. The Whipper Snipper reached to within two feet of those ruddy weeds!

Controlling her temper, she bundled everything up and proceeded back up the lane, dragging the almost-long-enough cords behind her and holding the machine with both arms. As she passed by the butternut tree a saucy little squirrel chattered at her in a mocking fashion. She replied with some nasty words of her own. She then proceeded to spend over half an hour returning the extension cords to their proper places and muttering to herself about her predicament. This activity cleared her head somewhat and helped her to determine her next step in the fight against the burdocks.

She grabbed her scissors and made her fifth trip down the lane, which by now, was starting to feel longer with each journey. With quiet, controlled precision she trimmed the long weeds around the flowers and then leaned over to tackle the burdocks with her trusty scissors. Then she slipped. With a slow roll, similar to the roll that high jumpers use as they clear the bar, she fell sideways and tumbled down, down, down. It seemed to her that it was all happening in slow motion as she plunged to the bottom of the deep ditch.

Out of the corner of her eye, she saw a car drive by and prayed silently that it wasn't someone she knew who might have witnessed her fall from grace. She focused her energy on getting out of the ditch. The sides of the ditch were quite steep and at first she considered crawling on her hands and knees at the bottom of the ditch until she reached the neighbour's lane, where it wasn't quite as steep. On second thought, she realized that she would never make it that far so she dug her toes in and grunting, huffing and puffing, climbed upwards until at last she was upright beside the still uncut burdocks.

Just then a car appeared and after a few minutes a woman got out and approached her. *"Oh my dear. Are you all right? We were driving by and saw you fall so we came back to see if you needed help."*

Irma replied that she was fine and thanked the woman profusely for her thoughtfulness. It was fortunate that Irma didn't need the stranger's help because although this good Samaritan was willing to help, she must have been around 80 years old and used a cane. Her passenger in the car looked to be about 90.

Irma walked up the lane for the sixth time and the same bold squirrel appeared and chattered at her again. She kicked some stones at it and the creature skittered away. She was in no mood right then to be one with nature. All of God's living creatures had best steer clear of her for a while.

Irma, the staunch and persistent senior, experienced no soreness or bruises from her tumble in the ditch and had remained as intact as those dreaded burdocks. She felt it wiser to return to her philosophy of *"live and let live"*.

This Serious Business Of Humour

On average, little children laugh about 300 times a day. Adults, on the other hand, laugh about 12 times a day. Something happens during the passage of time that takes away our playfulness and joy. We lose the sense of fun because life happens and life isn't always fun and games: we grow up, we have duties, we get sick, we experience losses, both big and small and things hurt. After a while the things that hurt, start to dull the joy. However, both pain and joy are a part of our human existence and we're going to experience them all our lives. In Catherine Ripplinger Fenwick's book, *Healing With Humour*, she states that laughter can be a First Aid Kit.

During our life we will face both opportunities and crises. If we choose to focus all our attention on the crises, we will experience more fear and pain. If we focus on the opportunities, we get more joy and laughter. So which is the wisest thing to do? It doesn't take a rocket scientist to figure that one out. It's the old concept of a glass being half full or half empty. My aunt would watch the weather forecast and note that there was an 80% chance of sun and a 20% chance of rain, and then bemoan the fact that it was going to rain. She always looked on the pessimistic side of things and strangely enough she was often sick. It is said that pessimistic people are more inclined to illness than optimists are.

An article in the April 2, 2002 issue of *The Ottawa Citizen* had this headline: *Humour Eases Aging Pains*. In it, Korky Vann cites several studies showing the benefits of laughter. Research indicates that laughing enhances your immune system, reduces stress and increases tolerance to pain. The article quotes statements by well-known people on the topic of the aging process. In one of them, Claude Pepper stated that a stockbroker encouraged him to buy stock that would triple every year. His response was, *"At my age I don't even buy green bananas!"*

Groucho Marx said, *"Last night I had a typical cholesterol-free dinner—baked squash, skimmed milk, and gelatin. I'm sure this will not make me live longer, but I know it's going to seem longer."* The article makes the observation that some parts of growing older are a real pain, but seeing the humour in them, makes the process easier to deal with.

Perhaps you have heard or have even used the following statements. *Life isn't meant to be all fun and games. Get your work done first and then play. Grow up already. Act your age.*

Out of the Mouths of Babes

I taught kindergarten for many years and found life in a classroom to be rife with funny events. I recall one little boy acting silly and actually said to him, *"Don't be so childish Sammy!"* It immediately struck me that he *was* just a child and was doing what children do. I never made that mistake again!

I recorded many of these funny events in a book I published entitled, *Out of the Mouths of Babes*. It consists of humourous incidents involving four- and five-year-olds. I only included the printable ones, but have enough left over to publish an x-rated book! One of my favourite anecdotes was the one about Jake and his mom. Jake's mom didn't appear for her duties one day as the Helping Mom. I asked Jake why his mom hadn't come and he replied, *"I think she has rabies!"* This same little boy gave me a Christmas gift in a pretty bag. I thanked him for the gift and commented on how pretty the bag was. He responded, *"I think my mom wants the bag back!"*

Another story involves Travis. He was playing with the big trucks and Sally was in his way. Travis yelled at Sally, *"Get out of my way you, you, you senior citizen!"*

Life seems to be all fun and games when you're in kindergarten, but as an adult it isn't all gloom and doom. When we accept life with dignity and hope, we're better able to get through the rough times and return to the joy that life can bring.

Churchly Humour

Sometimes things seem funnier when we are not in a position to laugh out loud and must exhibit some restraint, such as at church. One Sunday, our minister announced in his funereal voice, *"Please pick up your pamphlets before you pass out!"* That caused my sister and I to giggle and of course for Mother to give us the "eye".

My husband tells the strange but true story of two young lads who were misbehaving in the back pew of the church during a service. The Reverend endured the ruckus as long as he could, but finally strutted down the aisle. He grabbed the two boys and declared, *"I may not be able to perform miracles, but I can cast out devils."* He opened the church doors and tossed the boys out.

Stick with Humour—It's Just as Good for you as Oat Bran

Studies show that laughing is a healthy activity, probably as good for you as a generous serving of oat bran.

Catherine Ripplinger Fenwick states in her book, *Healing With Humour,* that tears and laughter are born of the same parents—they are two sides of the same coin and both cleanse the body from the inside. We often use these two methods to express our emotions. We don't always cry from pain or laugh from happiness. Sometimes we cry at weddings and laugh at funerals. It is often said that we can't grieve and laugh at the same time, but Fenwick believes that we can't grieve fully without laughter. The pain would be unbearable. Laughter and tears are ways of making intense emotions tolerable.

A sense of humour helps us through difficult times and makes the good times even better. The ability to laugh shows that we are on the right path towards leading a healthy life. Humour is everywhere—you just have to find it. Look for it! Create it! Spread it around! My hope is that the stories in this book will make you healthier by causing you to smile, titter or even giggle, and that will be just as good for you as many servings of oat bran!

Order Form

Please send me__________copies of
Growing Up Rural @ $9.95 Cdn. each.
For shipping and handling add $3.00 Cdn. per book.

Please send me__________copies of
Rural Reflections @ $9.95 Cdn. each.
For shipping and handling add $3.00 Cdn. per book.

Total amount:______________

Please complete this form and mail it to:

Isobel Eastman
5982 Prince of Wales Drive
North Gower, ON
K0A 2T0
Tel: 613-489-3276
e-mail: isobeleastman@rogers.com

❑ Enclosed is my cheque or money order.

Please send my book(s) to:

Name ________________________________

Address ______________________________

____

City _________________________________

Province _____________________________

Tel: (   ) __________________________